top SHELF
ADVANCED ALGEBRA

$$2x+10=6x-4$$

$$\sqrt[5]{64x^{10}y^{7}}$$

$$2|x-7|=26 \div 2$$

WALCH PUBLISHING

Katherine & Scott Robillard

The classroom teacher may reproduce materials in this book for classroom use only.
The reproduction of any part for an entire school or school system is strictly prohibited.
No part of this publication may be transmitted, stored, or recorded in any form
without written permission from the publisher.

1   2   3   4   5   6   7   8   9   10

ISBN 0-8251-5034-5

Copyright © 2005
J. Weston Walch, Publisher
P.O. Box 658 • Portland, Maine 04104-0658
walch.com

Printed in the United States of America

Contents

To the Teacher

Creative problem solving, precise reasoning, effective communication, and alertness to the reasonableness of results are some of the essential areas of mathematics that educators have specified as necessary in the development of all students to function effectively in this century. It is in the spirit of the aforementioned competencies that *Top Shelf Math* is offered to teachers of mathematics.

Top Shelf Math is intended to help students become better problem solvers. The problems presented in this format are challenging, interesting, and can easily be blended into the teaching styles and strategies of teachers who are seeking supplementary problems that support and enhance the curriculum being taught.

In general, the topics selected for each of the major content areas of *Top Shelf Math* are typical of those found in the curricula of similarly named courses offered at the high school and early college level. All of the problems presented can be used by the teacher to help his or her students improve their problem-solving skills without slowing the pace of the course in which the students are enrolled.

Other areas of utilization of the problems presented in *Top Shelf Math* could be by teachers to help prepare their students for achievement tests and advanced-placement tests. Math-team coaches will find these problems especially useful as they prepare their students for math competitions. It is recommended that students save the problems and solutions presented in *Top Shelf Math* because they provide a rich resource of mathematical

skills and strategies that will be useful for preparing to take standardized tests and enrollment in future mathematics courses.

Mathematical thought along with the notion of problem solving is playing an increasingly important role in nearly all phases of human endeavor. The problems presented in *Top Shelf Math* help provide the teacher with a mechanism for the students to witness a variety of applications in a wide sphere of real-life settings.

In problems requiring a calculator solution, it is recommended that only College Board-approved calculators be used. In addition, some problems will suggest that a calculator not be used and that the solution will require an algebraic procedure.

The approach for solving the problems presented in *Top Shelf Math* is consistent with emphasis by national mathematics organizations for reform in mathematics teaching and learning, content, and application by taking advantage of today's technological tools that are available to most if not all high school and college students enrolled in similarly named courses. *Top Shelf Math* provides the teacher with a balance of using these tools as well as well-established approaches to problem solving.

We hope that you will find the problems useful as general information as well as in preparation for higher-level coursework and testing. For additional books in the *Top Shelf Math* series, visit our web site at walch.com.

INSTRUCTION

Linear Equations

> ## A linear equation normally has only one solution or value that makes the statement true.

An **equation** is a mathematical statement in which one side equals the other side. A **linear equation** is one that contains only **variables** to the first degree. That means that you will not see any variables raised to any powers other than one. A linear equation normally has only one solution or value that makes the statement true.

When solving linear equations, use inverse operations applied to BOTH sides of the equal or inequality sign. The inverse operations "undo" the operations in the problem so you can find the solution, and apply it to both sides to keep the statement balanced. Your goal when solving a linear equation is to get the variable to one side and the numbers to the other. An easy way to check to be sure that your work is correct is to plug your solution into the original equation for whatever variable you were solving for. The equation will be a true statement if your solution is correct.

Example 1

Solving a linear equation with variables on both sides.

Solve: $2x + 10 = 6x - 4$

1. In order to gather the variables on one side, subtract $2x$ from both sides. Once you do this, combine like terms:

$$2x - 2x + 10 = 6x - 2x - 4 \qquad \Rightarrow \qquad 10 = 4x - 4$$

2. Next, to gather the numbers on the other side, add 4 to both sides and combine like terms:

$$10 + 4 = 4x \qquad \Rightarrow \qquad 14 = 4x$$

3. Last, isolate the x completely; to get the solution, we must divide both sides by 4. Remember to reduce any fractions:

$$\frac{14}{4} = \frac{4x}{4} \qquad \Rightarrow \qquad \frac{7}{2} = x$$

The solution to the equation is $x = \frac{7}{2}$.

A few notes to remember:

- It does not matter what side the variables are on and what side the numbers are on. It is just important to separate the numbers and the variables.

- You must apply the inverse operation to every term in your equation.

- You can only combine like terms.

- Your goal is to isolate the variable, meaning get the variable by itself on one side.

Example 2

Solving a linear equation using the distributive property to get rid of parentheses.

Solve: $4(3x - 6) = -(-2x + 14)$

1. Before gathering the variable on one side, apply the distributive property to clear all parentheses:

   $12x - 24 = 2x - 14$

2. To gather the variable on one side, subtract $2x$ from both sides:

   $12x - 2x - 24 = 2x - 2x - 14 \quad \Rightarrow \quad 10x - 24 = -14$

3. Now, add 24 to both sides to move all the numbers to the right side of the equation:

   $10x - 24 + 24 = -14 + 24 \quad \Rightarrow \quad 10x = 10$

4. Last, divide both sides by 10 to isolate the variable:

   $$\frac{10x}{10} = \frac{10}{10} \quad \Rightarrow \quad x = 1$$

The solution to the equation is $x = 1$.

Remember, you can check any solution by plugging it back into the original equation. If the solution is correct, you should get a true statement when you plug the solution in for the variable. This is something that should be done for every equation you solve. Let's check your work for the preceding example:

Verify that $x = 1$ is the solution to the equation: $4(3x - 6) = -(-2x + 14)$.

1. Plug 1 in for every x in the equation:

    $$4(3(1) - 6) = -(-2(1) + 14)$$

2. Simplify, using the correct order of operations:

    $$4(3 - 6) = -(-2 + 14) \qquad \Rightarrow \qquad 4(-3) = -(12)$$

    $$\Rightarrow -12 = -12$$

3. Because $-12 = -12$, your solution is correct.

When solving equations with decimals or fractions, there are a couple of tricks you can apply to make your computation easier:

Fractions: If an equation contains one or more fractions, you can multiply every term by the least common denominator of all the fractions and clear them.

Example 3

Solving a linear equation that contains fractions.

Solve: $\dfrac{1}{2}x - 5 = -4x + \dfrac{5}{3}$

1. Examine all the denominators and determine the least common denominator:

    The least common denominator for 2 and 3 is 6.

2. Multiply every term by the least common denominator:

    $$(6)\dfrac{1}{2}x - (6)5 = (6)(-4x) + (6)\dfrac{5}{3} \quad \Rightarrow \quad 3x - 30 = -24x + 10$$

3. Finally, solve the equation following the steps from above. Be sure to check your results to be certain that your solution is correct.

Decimals: If an equation contains one or more terms with decimals, you can multiply every term by the largest power of ten required to clear the decimal from each term.

Example 4

Solving a linear equation with decimals.

Solve: $-4.2x + 12 = -6.05x + 21$

1. Examine every term that contains a decimal point and determine the smallest power of 10 that would clear every decimal point:

   Multiplying by 10 would clear the decimal in the term $-4.2x$, but would not clear the decimal point in the term $-6.05x$. Therefore, every term in this equation must be multiplied by 100 in order to clear every decimal point.

2. Multiply every term in the equation by the appropriate power of 10:

   $(100)(-4.2x) + (100)12 = (100)(-6.05x) + (100)(21) \quad \Rightarrow$

   $-420x + 1200 = -605x + 2100$

3. Finally, solve the equation following the steps from above. Be sure to check your results to be certain that your solution is correct.

Although a linear equation normally has only one solution, there are a couple of special cases to watch out for. You will know that you are dealing with one of these special cases if your variable cancels out and you end up with a statement that contains only numbers.

No solution: An equation has no solution when inverse operations cause the variable to cancel out and you are left with a false statement. This means that no value of x, or whatever variable you are using, will make the statement true. In this case, you need to indicate that the equation has no solution.

Infinite solutions: An equation has infinite solutions when inverse operations cause the variables to cancel out, leaving a true statement. This means that any value of x, or whatever variable you are using, will make the statement true. In this case, you need to indicate that the equation has infinite solutions. Sometimes an equation that has infinite solutions is referred to as an **identity**.

Examples 5 and 6

Solving equations with no solution or infinite solutions.

The following examples will illustrate the results of applying the preceding steps mentioned to equations with no solutions or infinite solutions.

Solve: $7(x + 1) - 3x = 5 + 4(x - 1)$

$$7x + 7 - 3x = 5 + 4x - 4 \qquad \Rightarrow \qquad 4x + 7 = 1 + 4x$$

$$4x - 4x = 1 - 7 \qquad\qquad\qquad \Rightarrow \qquad 0 = -6$$

The fact that the variable has canceled out indicates that this is one of the two special cases discussed above. Because 0 does not equal -6, this equation has no solution. No value of x will make the equation true.

Solve: $6x - 4 = 2(3x - 2)$

$$6x - 4 = 6x \quad 4 \qquad\qquad \Rightarrow \qquad 6x - 6x = -4 + 4$$

$$0 = 0$$

The fact that the variable has canceled out indicates that this is one of the two special cases discussed above. Because 0 does equal 0, this equation has infinite solutions. That means ANY value of x will make the equation true.

 **Practice Activities**

Solve the following equations.

1. $3x - 2(4 - x) = 17$ 2. $3x - \dfrac{1}{5} = 2x + \dfrac{3}{10}$

3. $6x - 4 = 2(3x + 8)$ 4. $3x - 2(5x - 8) = 12x + 32$

Verify that each value is the correct solution for the given equation.

5. $\dfrac{2x}{3} + \dfrac{x}{6} = \dfrac{5}{2}$ $x = 3$

6. $4x - 2(5x - 8) = 5(-2x + 4)$ $x = 1$

7. Give an example of an equation that has infinite solutions.

8. Give an example of an equation that has no solution.

 **INSTRUCTION**

Linear Inequalities

> **A linear inequality is a statement in which the two sides are not equal.**

Like a linear equation, a **linear inequality** does not contain any variables raised to a power other than one. However, a linear inequality is a statement in which the two sides are not equal. One side can be less than (<), greater than (>), less than or equal to (≤), or greater than or equal to (≥) the other side. Unlike linear equations, linear inequalities often have many values of the given variables that will correctly solve the inequality. The solutions to linear inequalities normally represent a range of values that will make the given statement true.

When solving linear inequalities, use many of the same steps and procedures involved with solving linear equations. When solving a linear inequality, apply inverse operations to both sides of the inequality sign until we have isolated the variable on one side of the inequality sign.

Hint: While it does not matter what side of the inequality sign the variable is on, it is sometimes easier to comprehend the solution if the variable is isolated on the left-hand side.

The solution to a linear inequality can be represented by a graph on a number line. Closed and open circles are used in conjunction with arrows to indicate which values will solve the inequality. If the boundary number is not included in the solution, an open circle is used. If the boundary number is included in the solution, a closed circle is used. For instance:

If the solution to an inequality is $x > -5$, any value of *x greater* than 5 will solve the inequality. Since -5 is not part of the solution, draw an open circle at -5 and an arrow pointing right. All values to the right of -5 will solve the inequality.

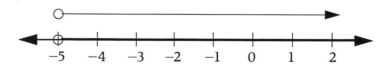

If the solution to an inequality is $x \le 8$, any value of *x* less than or equal to 8 will solve the inequality. 8 is a part of the solution, so draw a closed circle at 8 and an arrow pointing left. All values to the left of 8, and including 8, will solve the inequality.

7

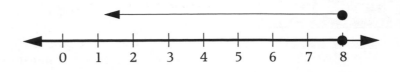

One important rule to remember when solving inequalities is:

When multiplying or dividing by a negative value, change the direction of the inequality sign.

$$-3x \leq 30 \Rightarrow \frac{-3x}{-3} \geq \frac{30}{-3}$$

Adding or subtracting values from either side of an inequality does not affect the direction of the inequality sign.

As with linear equations, the solution to a linear inequality can also be checked by plugging into the original inequality. Any value indicated by the solution should make a true statement when plugged into the inequality.

Although a linear inequality normally has only a specified range of solutions, there are a couple of special cases to watch out for. You will know that you are dealing with one of these special cases if your variable cancels out and you end up with a statement that contains only numbers.

No solution: An inequality has no solution when the inverse operations cause the variable to cancel out and you are left with a false statement. This means that no value of *x,* or whatever variable you are using, will make your statement true. In this case, you need to indicate that your inequality has no solution.

Infinite solutions: Your inequality has infinite solutions when your inverse operations cause your variables to cancel out and you are left with a true statement. This means that any value of *x,* or whatever variable you are using, will make your statement true. In this case, you need to indicate that your inequality has infinite solutions. You may also indicate that "all real numbers" will solve the inequality.

Example 1

Solve and graph the following inequality.

$3x - 22 < 5(2 - x)$

1. Apply the distributive property and then isolate the x on the left-hand side by applying inverse operations:

   $3x - 22 < 10 - 5x$ $\Rightarrow$ $3x + 5x < 10 + 22$

   $8x < 32$ $\Rightarrow$ $\dfrac{8x}{8} < \dfrac{32}{8}$

   $x < 4$

2. Determine what type of circle should be used, and graph the solution on a number line:

   Because all numbers less than 4 are only part of the solution, an open circle should be used as part of the graph. An arrow pointing left will indicate that all values to the left of 4 are part of the solution.

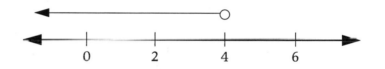

3. To check the solution, plug any value to the left of 4 on the number line into the original inequality:

   $2(2) - 22 < 5(2 - 2)$ $\rightarrow$ $4 - 22 < 5(0)$

   $-18 < 0$

   Because -18 is less than 0, our solution is correct. Any value to the left of 4, or any value less than 4, will satisfy your inequality.

Example 2

Solve and graph the following inequality.

$-18 - 5x \geq 52$

1. Isolate the x on the right-hand side by applying inverse operations to both sides of the inequality:

$$-18 + 18 - 5x \geq 52 + 18 \qquad \Rightarrow \qquad -5x \geq 70$$

Remember to change the direction of the inequality because you are dividing by a -5.

$$\frac{-5x}{-5} \leq \frac{70}{-5} \qquad \Rightarrow \qquad x \leq -14$$

2. Determine what type of circle should be used, and graph the solution on a number line:

Because all numbers less than -14 and including -14 are part of the solution, a closed circle should be used as part of the graph. An arrow pointing left will indicate that -14 and all values to the left of -14 are part of the solution.

Examples 3 and 4

The following examples will illustrate the results of solving a linear inequality with no solution and infinite solutions.

Example 3

Solving a linear inequality with no solutions.

Solve: $2(2x - 3) \geq 8 + 4x$

1. Distribute to clear all parentheses:

$$4x - 6 \geq 8 + 4x$$

2. Apply inverse operations to both sides of the inequality sign to isolate the variable:

$$4x - 4x - 6 + 6 \geq 8 + 6 + 4x - 4x \qquad \Rightarrow \qquad 0 \geq 14$$

Because the variable has canceled out, you know you have a special case. Because 0 is NOT greater than 14, the statement is false, and therefore the inequality has no solutions. That means that no value of x will plug into this inequality and result in a true statement.

Example 4

Solving an inequality with all solutions.

Solve: $-3x + 14 < -3(x - 8)$

1. Distribute to clear all parentheses:

   $-3x + 14 < -3x + 24$

2. Apply inverse operations to both sides of the inequality sign to isolate the variable:

   $-3x + 3x + 14 - 14 < -3x + 3x + 24 - 14$ 　　$\Rightarrow$ 　　$0 < 10$

Because the variable has canceled out, you know that you have a special case. Because 0 IS less than 10, the statement is true and therefore the inequality has infinite solutions. That means that ANY value of x will plug into this inequality and result in a true statement.

Practice Activities

Solve and graph the following inequalities.

1. $\frac{1}{2}x + 6 > 4$

2. $-7.9 < -2.1x + 4.7$

3. $4(-x + 3) \leq -5x + 5$

4. $-(5x - 7) + 10 \geq -3(x - 3)$

Determine if the following inequalities have no solution or infinite solutions.

5. $6(2x - 3) > -4(-3x + 6) - 2$

6. $\frac{1}{2}x - 16 \leq \frac{1}{4}(2x + 8)$

7. $2.4x - 3.9 < .2(12x + 7)$

8. $-2x - 6 \geq -3x - (-x + 6)$

INSTRUCTION

Compound Inequalities

A **compound inequality** is made up of two inequalities joined by the words "and" or "or." These joining words determine the solution to the problem. If the inequalities are joined with "and," the solution must include only values of the variable that work for both inequalities. If the inequalities are joined with "or," the solution must include any value of the variable that works for at least one side. Each side of the inequality is solved by following the steps for solving a single linear inequality.

Note: Inequalities written as $0 < 2x - 16 \leq 10$ are solved as "and" inequalities. You may either solve it as one statement, adding 16 to 0 and 10, then dividing each part by 2, or you can divide the statement into two separate statements joined by "and":

$$0 < 2x - 16 \quad and \quad 2x - 16 \leq 10.$$

A simple way to determine the solution set to a compound inequality is to graph the solutions to both sides of the inequality on the same number line. For "and" compound inequalities, the final solution must only include values in the area where the two graphs overlap. For "or" compound inequalities, the final solution includes any value that is a solution to either side. In this case, if the value is covered by either graph, it is part of the entire solution.

Just like single linear inequalities, it is possible to get no solution or all real numbers when solving a compound inequality. Normally, if two arrows are going away from each other with no overlap, and the compound inequality is joined with "and," the problem has no solution. If the arrows are pointing toward each other and the inequality is joined with "or," the solution is all real numbers.

> **A compound inequality is made up of two inequalities joined by the words "and" or "or."**

13

Example 1

Solve and graph the following compound inequality.

$4x - 5 > 16 - 3x$ *and* $7x - (5 - 2x) < 31$

1. Solve one side of the inequality:

   $4x + 3x - 5 > 16 - 3x + 3x$ $\Rightarrow$ $7x - 5 > 16$

   $7x - 5 + 5 > 16 + 5$ $\Rightarrow$ $7x > 21$

   $\dfrac{7x}{7} > \dfrac{21}{7}$ $\Rightarrow$ $x > 3$

2. Solve the other side:

   $7x - 5 + 2x < 31$ $\Rightarrow$ $9x - 5 + 5 < 31 + 5$

   $9x < 36$ $\Rightarrow$ $\dfrac{9x}{9} < \dfrac{36}{9}$

   $x < 4$

3. Graph both results on a number line:

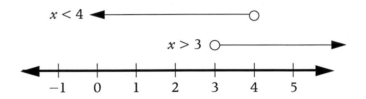

4. Determine the final solution:

   Because this inequality is joined with "and," your solution can only include values that solve BOTH inequalities. Therefore, look for the overlap of the two arrows drawn above.

   The overlap occurs between 3 and 4. So, any value between 3 and 4 is a solution to the compound inequality. The solution would look like this:

   $3 < x < 4$

   And its graph is:

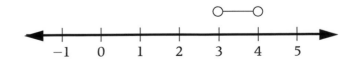

Example 2

Solve and graph the following inequality.

$3 + 5x \leq 2x - 15$ *or* $9 - 9x < 18$

1. Solve one side of the inequality:

    $3 - 3 + 5x - 2x \leq 2x - 2x - 15 - 3$ $\Rightarrow$ $3x \leq -18$

    $\dfrac{3x}{3} \leq \dfrac{-18}{3}$ $\Rightarrow$ $x \leq -6$

2. Solve the other side:

    $9 - 9 - 9x < 18 - 9$ $\Rightarrow$ $-9x < 9$

    $\dfrac{-9x}{-9} < \dfrac{9}{-9}$ $\Rightarrow$ $x > -1$

3. Graph both results on a number line:

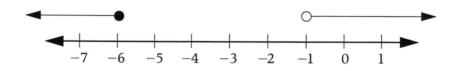

4. Determine your final solution:

    Because these inequalities are joined by "or," any value that is covered by either arrow must be included in the final solution. Therefore, all values of x less than or equal to -6 and all values of x greater than -1 are part of the solution.

    Your final answer would look like this:

    $x \leq -6$ *or* $x > -1$

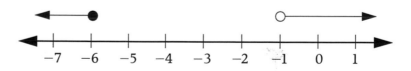

Example 3

Determine the final solution from these results.

a. $x \leq -2$ *and* $x > 0$

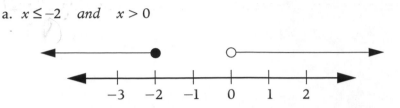

Because this is an "and" inequality, the solution can only include values of x that fall in the overlap between the two arrows. Because there is no overlap, there is no solution.

b. $x > 5$ *or* $x < 9$

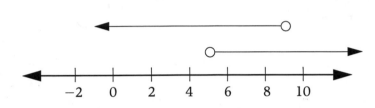

Because this is an "or" inequality, the solution must include any value that is covered (or will be covered) by either arrow. Remember that both arrows extend in one direction. Because the arrows are pointing toward each other, all parts of the number line will eventually be covered by one of the arrows. Therefore, the inequality has all real numbers for a solution.

c. $x \geq 6$ *and* $x > 9$

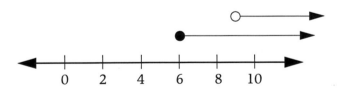

Because this is an "and" inequality, the solution must only include values of x that fall in the overlapped region. In this case, the overlap begins at 9 and continues right infinitely. Therefore, any value greater than 9 will be part of our final solution: $x > 9$.

How would this answer change if the results were joined by "or"?

π TRY IT   **Practice Activities**

Solve and graph the following compound inequalities. Be sure to indicate a final solution.

1. $3(x - 2) > 18x + 9$ *and* $-4(2x + 1) \leq 20$

2. $10x - 16 < 4(2x - 3)$ *or* $3x \geq -4x + 28$

3. $2(2x - 7) + 7 \leq 10$ *or* $7 + x > -3$

4. $-5 \leq -x - 6$ *and* $-x + 6 < 0$

Graph the results, and determine the final answers.

5. $x > -4$ *and* $x \leq -4$ 6. $x < -2$ *or* $x \leq 4$

INSTRUCTION

Absolute Value Equations and Inequalities

The **absolute value** of a number is the distance that number is away from zero. The distance is always represented as a positive number; therefore, the absolute value of a number will always be positive. $|\,|$ is the symbol used to represent absolute value. To find the value of x when $|x| = 5$, you need to find the number or numbers that are five units away from zero. In this case, there are two answers: $x = 5$ and $x = -5$. To solve an absolute value equation, you should first isolate the absolute value by moving everything outside of the $|\,|$ to the other side of the equation by using inverse operations. Next, rewrite the absolute value equation twice as linear equations. The first equation will look the same, while the second equation will change the value on the side opposite what was previously inside the absolute value symbols as its opposite. This will allow you to find both values for x that can satisfy the equation.

When solving absolute value inequalities, you would follow the same steps as solving absolute value equations except, when you rewrite the inequalities twice, not only do you change the second inequality's number on the right side to its opposite but you also must change its inequality symbol to its opposite, too.

> **The absolute value of a number is the distance that number is away from zero.**

Example 1

Find the solutions of the equation $5|x - 4| - 3 = 47$.

Solution:

1. Isolate the absolute value symbol by first adding 3 to both sides and then dividing both sides by 5.

$$5|x-4| - 3 + 3 = 47 + 3 \qquad \Rightarrow \qquad 5|x-4| = 50$$

$$5 \div 5|x-4| = 50 \div 5 \qquad \Rightarrow \qquad |x-4| = 10$$

2. Rewrite the equation twice without the absolute value symbols. Write one of the equations with the right side equaling 10 and the other equation having the right side equaling −10. This will allow you to find both solutions that satisfy the equation.

$$x - 4 = 10 \qquad\qquad\qquad x - 4 = -10$$

18

3. Solve both equations for x by adding 4 to both sides.

$x - 4 + 4 = 10 + 4$ $\qquad\qquad\qquad$ $x - 4 + 4 = -10 + 4$

$x = 14$ $\qquad\qquad\qquad\qquad\qquad$ $x = -6$

4. Check your answers by placing both solutions back into the original equation and solving.

$5|14 - 4| - 3 = 47$ $\qquad\qquad\qquad$ $5|-6 - 4| - 3 = 47$

$5|10| - 3 = 47$ $\qquad\qquad\qquad\quad$ $5|-10| - 3 = 47$

$5 \cdot 10 - 3 = 47$ $\qquad\qquad\qquad\quad$ $5 \cdot 10 - 3 = 47$

$50 - 3 = 47$ $\qquad\qquad\qquad\qquad$ $50 - 3 = 47$

$47 = 47$ $\qquad\qquad\qquad\qquad\qquad$ $47 = 47$

Example 2

Find the solutions of the equation $2|x - 7| + 5 = 31$.

Solution:

1. Isolate the absolute value symbol by first subtracting 5 from both sides and then dividing both sides by 5.

$2|x - 7| + 5 - 5 = 31 - 5$ $\quad\Rightarrow\quad$ $2|x - 7| = 26$

$2 \div 2|x - 7| = 26 \div 2$ $\qquad\Rightarrow\quad$ $|x - 7| = 13$

2. Rewrite the equation twice without the absolute value symbols. Write one of the equations with the right side equaling 10 and the other equation having the right side equaling −10. This will allow you to find both solutions that satisfy the equation.

$x - 7 = 13$ $\qquad\qquad\qquad\qquad$ $x - 7 = -13$

3. Solve both equations for x by adding 7 to both sides.

$x - 7 + 7 = 13 + 7$ $\qquad\qquad\qquad$ $x - 7 + 7 = -13 + 7$

$x = 20$ $\qquad\qquad\qquad\qquad\qquad$ $x = -6$

4. Check both of your solutions by placing them back into the original equation and solving.

$$2|20 - 7| + 5 = 31 \qquad\qquad 2|-6 - 7| + 5 = 31$$

$$2(13) + 5 = 31 \qquad\qquad\quad 2(13) + 5 = 31$$

$$31 = 31 \qquad\qquad\qquad\quad 31 = 31$$

Example 3

Find the solutions of the inequality $\dfrac{1}{3}|x + 6| - 13 \geq -8$.

Solution:

1. Isolate the absolute value symbol by first adding 13 to both sides and then multiplying both sides by 3.

$$\frac{1}{3}|x + 6| - 13 + 13 \geq -8 + 13 \quad \Rightarrow \quad \frac{1}{3}|x + 6| \geq 5$$

$$3 \cdot \frac{1}{3}|x + 6| \geq 5 \cdot 3 \qquad\qquad \Rightarrow \quad |x + 6| \geq 15$$

2. Rewrite the inequalities twice without the absolute value symbols. Write one of the inequalities with the right side being greater than or equal to 15 and the other inequality having the right side being less than or equal to −15. This will allow you to find both solutions that satisfy the inequalities.

$$x + 6 \geq 15 \qquad\qquad\qquad x + 6 \leq -15$$

3. Solve both inequalities for x by subtracting 6 from both sides.

$$x + 6 - 6 \geq 15 - 6 \qquad\qquad x + 6 - 6 \leq -15 - 6$$

$$x \geq 9 \qquad\qquad\qquad\qquad x \leq -21$$

4. Check the endpoints of your solutions by placing them back into the original inequality and solving.

$$\frac{1}{3}|9 + 6| - 13 \geq -8 \qquad\qquad \frac{1}{3}|-21 + 6| - 13 \geq -8$$

$$\frac{1}{3}|15| - 13 \geq -8 \qquad\qquad \frac{1}{3}|-15| - 13 \geq -8$$

$$\frac{1}{3}(15) - 13 \geq -8 \qquad\qquad \frac{1}{3}(15) - 13 \geq -8$$

$$5 - 13 \geq -8 \qquad\qquad\qquad 5 - 13 \geq -8$$

$$-8 \geq -8 \qquad\qquad\qquad\quad -8 \geq -8$$

5. Once you have checked some of your solutions, graph them on a number line.

Practice Activities

Solve each absolute value equation.

1. $4|x - 3| + 9 = 33$

2. $\dfrac{1}{5}|x - 11| - 2 = 7$

3. $-3|x - 12| - 5 = -8$

4. $\dfrac{2}{3}|2x + 5| - 4 = 6$

Solve each absolute value inequality, and then graph the solution on a number line.

5. $6|2x - 3| + 7 \le 13$

6. $\dfrac{3}{4}|x + 13| + 8 \ge 32$

7. $-2|x - 17| - 6 > -14$

8. $4|x + 19| - 2 < 30$

INSTRUCTION

The Graphing Method

A system of equations is two or more equations. When solving a system, you are finding the point that satisfies both equations, or the *x* and *y* values that can be substituted back into both equations and make true statements. On a graph, it would be the point where the two lines intersect.

> **A system of equations is two or more equations.**

Solving a system has many practical applications, including finding the **break-even point** when comparing two things. In this section, you will solve a system of equations using the graphing method. You will also explore instances when a system has no solution or many solutions. To solve using the graphing method, start by getting both equations into slope-intercept form. Next, graph both equations on the same plane and locate the point where they intersect. Once you have found this point, you must test it in both equations; if it satisfies both equations, then you have found the correct solution.

Example 1

Find the solution of the system $3x + y = 6$ and $-2x + 3y = 7$ by using the graphing method.

Solution:

1. Put both equations into slope-intercept form by solving for *y*.

$$3x + y = 6$$
$$\underline{-3x \qquad -3x}$$

$$y = -3x + 6$$

$$-2x + 3y = 7$$
$$\underline{+2x \qquad +2x}$$

$$\frac{3}{3}y = \frac{2}{3}x + \frac{7}{3}$$

$$y = \frac{2}{3}x + 2\frac{1}{3}$$

2. Graph both lines on the same plane, and look for the point of intersection:

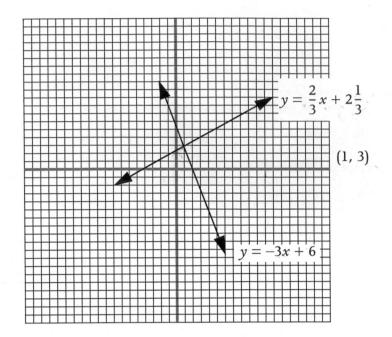

$$y = \frac{2}{3}x + 2\frac{1}{3}$$

(1, 3)

$$y = -3x + 6$$

3. Once you have found the point of intersection, check to see that it is the correct solution by testing the ordered pair in both equations.

point of intersection = (1, 3)

$3x + y = 6$	$-2x + 3y = 7$
$3(1) + 3 = 6$	$-2(1) + 3(3) = 7$
$6 = 6$	$-2 + 9 = 7$
	$7 = 7$

Example 2

Find the solution of the system $2x + y = 8$ and $4x + 2y = 4$ by using the graphing method.

Solution:

1. Put both equations into slope-intercept form by solving for y:

$$2x + y = 8$$
$$\underline{-2x \qquad -2x}$$
$$y = -2x + 8$$

$$4x + 2y = 4$$
$$\underline{-4x \qquad -4x}$$
$$\frac{2y}{2} = \frac{-4x}{2} + \frac{4}{2}$$
$$y = -2x + 2$$

2. Graph both lines on the same plane, and look for the point of intersection:

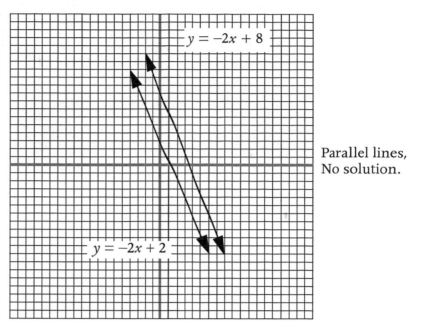

Parallel lines, No solution.

In this case, there is no solution because the two lines do not intersect; they are parallel. Parallel lines have no solution.

Example 3

Find the solution of the system $-x + y = -1$ and $4x - 4y = 4$ by using the graphing method.

Solution:

1. Put both equations into slope-intercept form by solving for y:

$$-x + y = -1$$
$$\underline{+\,x \qquad\quad +\,x}$$

$$y = x - 1$$

$$4x - 4y = 4$$
$$\underline{-4x \qquad\quad -4x}$$

$$\frac{-4}{-4}y = \frac{-4}{-4}x + \frac{4}{-4}$$

$$y = x - 1$$

2. Graph both lines on the same plane, and look for the point of intersection:

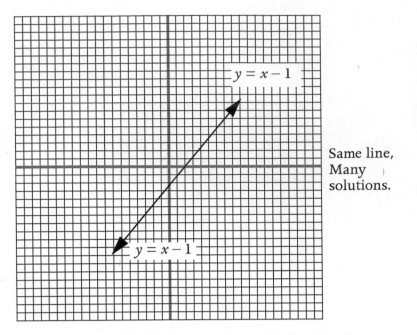

Same line,
Many
solutions.

In this example, the lines are on top of each other because they are the same line. Therefore, these two equations are said to have infinitely many solutions because they share all of the same points.

 **Practice Activities**

Solve using the graphing method.

1. $y = 4x - 2$
    $y = 2x$

2. $y = -x + 1$
    $y = 2x - 8$

3. $y = 2x + 2$
    $y = -2x - 6$

4. $4x - 2y = 18$
    $2x + 2y = 12$

5. $y = -3x + 6$
   $2x - y = -6$

6. $4x + 5y = -2$
   $2x + y = -4$

7. $4x - 2y = 6$
   $-6x + 3y = 12$

8. $y = -3x + 1$
   $-6x - 2y = -2$

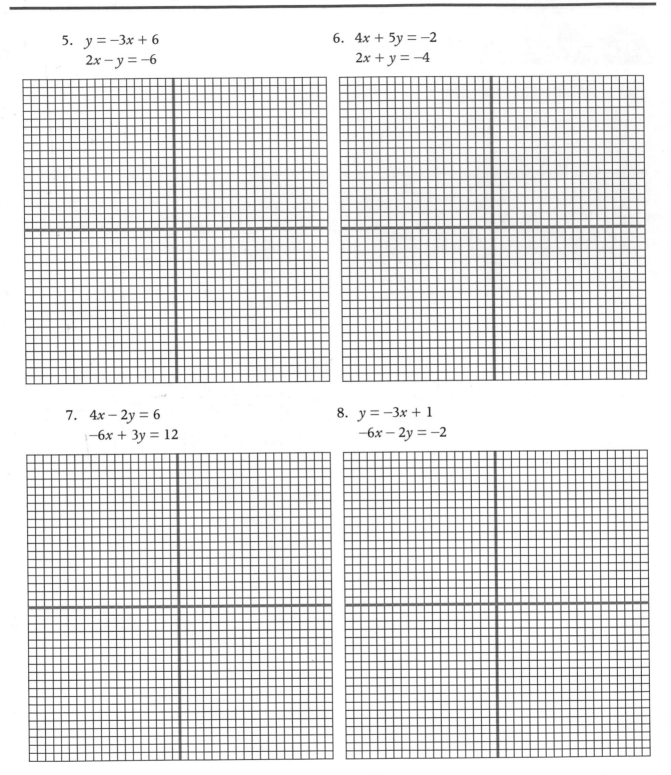

28

9. $x + y = -2$
$5x + 5y = -10$

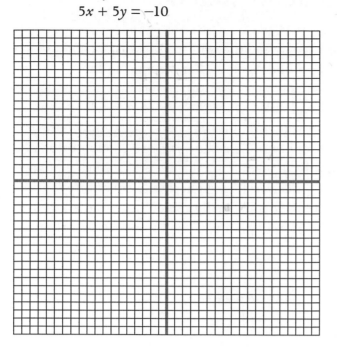

INSTRUCTION

The Substitution Method

A second method used to find the solution of a system of equations is the substitution method. To solve a system using the substitution method, you must first solve one of the two equations for either one of its variables. Once the chosen variable is by itself, substitute the solved equation into the other equation wherever the chosen variable appears. This allows you to eliminate one of the variables and solve the equation for the other. Once you have found a solution for that variable, go back and substitute that value into the equation you originally solved to get the solution for the other variable. This will give you an ordered-pair solution.

> To solve a system using the substitution method, you must first solve one of the two equations for either one of its variables.

Example 1

Find the solution of the system $2x + y = 7$ and $-2x + 2y = -4$ using the substitution method.

Solution:

1. Solve one of the equations for either variable. *Hint:* Look for a variable that has 1 as its **coefficient**. This variable would be the easiest to get by itself. In this example, it would be the y in the first equation.

   $$2x - 2x + y = 7 - 2x \quad \Rightarrow \quad y = -2x + 7$$

2. Substitute the solved equation into the other equation wherever the variable it equals appears. In this example, the $-2x + 7$ will substitute into the $-2x + 2y = -4$ for y.

   $$-2x + 2(-2x + 7) = -4$$

3. Solve the second equation.

   $$-2x + 2(-2x + 7) = -4$$
$-2x + 2(-2x + 7) = -4$	
$-2x - 4x + 14 = -4$	Distribute the 2.
$-6x + 14 = -4$	Combine like terms.
$-6x = -18$	Subtract 14.
$x = 3$	Divide by -6.

4. Substitute your value for x back into your solved equation to find the value of y.

$y = -2(3) + 7$
$y = -6 + 7$
$y = 1$

The point of intersection for this system is $(3,1)$.

Example 2

Find the solution of the system $3x - y = 6$ and $-3x + y = 2$, using the substitution method.

Solution:

1. Solve one of the equations for either variable. Remember, look for a variable that has 1 as its coefficient. This variable would be the easiest to get by itself. In this example, it would be the y in the second equation.

$-3x + 3x + y = 2 + 3x \implies y = 3x + 2$

2. Substitute the solved equation into the other equation wherever the variable it equals appears. In this example, the $3x + 2$ will substitute into the $3x - y = 6$ for y.

$3x - (3x + 2) = 6$

3. Solve the second equation.

$3x - (3x + 2) = 6$	
$3x - 3x - 2 = 6$	Distribute the $-$.
$-2 = 6$	Combine like terms.
$0 = 8$	Add 2.

In this example, both the x and the y variables were eliminated, leaving the problem with a statement that does not make sense: $0 = 8$. When variables are eliminated and the final result is a false statement, then the system has no solution. If we were to graph these two equations, they would be parallel lines.

Example 3

Find the solution of the system $x + y = 4$ and $3x + 3y = 12$, using the substitution method.

Solution:

1. Solve one of the equations for either variable. Remember to look for a variable that has 1 as its coefficient. This variable would be the easiest to get by itself. In this example, it would be the x or the y in the first equation.

   $$x + y - y = 4 - y \quad \Rightarrow \quad x = -y + 4$$

2. Substitute the solved equation into the other equation wherever the variable it equals appears. In this example, the $-y + 4$ will substitute into the $3x + 3y = 12$ for x.

   $$3(-y + 4) + 3y = 12$$

3. Solve the second equation.

$3(-y + 4) + 3y = 12$	
$-3y + 12 + 3y = 12$	Distribute the 3.
$12 = 12$	Combine like terms.
$0 = 0$	Subtract 12.

   In this example, both the x and the y variables were eliminated, leaving the problem with a sentence $0 = 0$. When the variables cancel and the final result is a true statement, the system has infinitely many solutions. If you were to graph these two equations, they would be the same line.

 **TRY IT**   **Practice Activities**

Solve using the substitution method.

1. $\begin{cases} y = 3x + 2 \\ 2x - 3y = 1 \end{cases}$

2. $\begin{cases} y = -x + 3 \\ x + 3y = 1 \end{cases}$

3. $\begin{cases} y = 4x - 1 \\ 2x - y = -3 \end{cases}$

4. $\begin{cases} 2x + 3y = 5 \\ x - 5y = 9 \end{cases}$

5. $\begin{cases} -x + 2y = 3 \\ 4x - 5y = -3 \end{cases}$

6. $\begin{cases} \dfrac{1}{2}x + y = 9 \\ 7x + 4y = 26 \end{cases}$

7. $\begin{cases} 2x + 4y = 8 \\ 3x + 6y = 6 \end{cases}$

8. $\begin{cases} 6x + 2y = 4 \\ -12x - 4y = -8 \end{cases}$

9. $\begin{cases} x + y = 9 \\ 2x + 2y = 18 \end{cases}$

INSTRUCTION

The Elimination Method

> The third way to solve a system of equations is by using the elimination method.

The third way to solve a system of equations is by using the elimination method. To solve a system using the elimination method, first write both equations in standard form, being sure to stack the two equations in order to add them together. The idea behind the elimination method is to have opposite coefficients for one of the sets of variables, so that adding the two equations eliminates that variable. In order to use the elimination method, you need either the x variables or y variables to have opposite coefficients. For this to happen, you may have to multiply the top equation, bottom equation, or both equations by a number in order to create opposite coefficients. Once you have opposite coefficients, you can add the two equations, which will eliminate one of the variables. This will allow you to find the value of one of the variables. Once you have the value for one variable, you can substitute that value back into any of the equations to find the value for the originally eliminated variable.

Example 1

Find the solution of the system $x + y = 6$ and $2x - y = 9$, by using the elimination method.

Solution:

1. Stack the two equations, lining up the variables on top of each other.

$$\begin{cases} x + y = 6 \\ 2x - y = 9 \end{cases}$$

2. Look for equivalent coefficients with opposite signs that will cancel when added together. Add the equations.

In this example, the y variables have opposite coefficients (-1 and 1), so you can add the two equations and eliminate the y variables.

$$\begin{array}{r} x + y = 6 \\ + \, 2x - y = 9 \\ \hline 3x = 15 \\ x = 5 \end{array}$$

3. Substitute your solution for x back into any of the equations, and solve to find the value of y.

$$\begin{array}{r} (5) + y = 6 \\ -5 \qquad -5 \\ \hline y = 1 \end{array}$$

The solution of this system is $(5,1)$.

Example 2

Find the solution of the system $6x - 4y = 10$ and $3x - 2y = -4$, by using the elimination method.

Solution:

1. Stack the two equations, lining up the variables on top of each other.

$$\begin{cases} 6x - 4y = 10 \\ 3x - 2y = -4 \end{cases}$$

2. Because neither of the variables have opposite coefficients, you will need to multiply the bottom equation by a number that will create opposite coefficients so you can eliminate either the x variables or the y variables.

In order to eliminate the x variables, you would multiply the bottom equation by -2 and then add the two equations.

Make sure you multiply every term in the equation by the constant you choose.

$$6x - 4y = 10 \quad \Rightarrow \quad 6x - 4y = 10$$

$$-2(3x - 2y = -4) \quad \Rightarrow \quad + \underline{-6x + 4y = 8}$$

$$0 = 18$$

In this example, both variables were canceled out, leaving a false statement, $0 = 18$. Therefore, there is no solution, and these two equations would graph to be parallel lines. If both variables canceled and the result was a true statement, for example, $0 = 0$, the lines would be the same and the system would have infinitely many solutions.

Example 3

Find the solution of the system $-2x + 3y = 5$ and $5x - 4y = -2$, by using the elimination method.

Solution:

1. Stack the two equations, lining up the variables on top of each other.

   $-2x + 3y = 5$

   $5x - 4y = -2$

2. Because neither of the variables have opposite coefficients, you will need to multiply both equations by numbers that will create opposite coefficients.

   In order to eliminate the x variables, you would multiply the top equation by 5 and the bottom by 2.

   $5(-2x + 3y = 5) \quad -10x + 15y = 25$

   $2(5x - 4y = -2) \quad + \underline{10x - 8y = -4} \quad$ Add the 2 equations together.

   $\qquad\qquad\qquad 7y = 21 \quad$ Solve for y.

   $\qquad\qquad\qquad y = 3$

3. Substitute your solution for y back into any of the equations to find the value of x.

$-2x + 3(3) = 5$

$-2x + 9 = 5$ Subtract 9.

$-2x = -4$ Divide by -2.

$x = 2$

The solution of this system is $(2, 3)$.

 **Practice Activities**

Solve using the elimination method.

1. $\begin{cases} 2x - 3y = 5 \\ -2x + y = -9 \end{cases}$

2. $\begin{cases} 5x - 4y = 6 \\ x + 4y = 6 \end{cases}$

3. $\begin{cases} 2x + 3y = 10 \\ x - y = 5 \end{cases}$

4. $\begin{cases} -5x + 7y = 11 \\ 3y - 5x = 19 \end{cases}$

5. $\begin{cases} -2x + 3y = 20 \\ 4x + 4y = -15 \end{cases}$

6. $\begin{cases} x - y = 17 \\ 2x - 12y = 4 \end{cases}$

7. $\begin{cases} -x + 2y = 4 \\ 2y - 4x = 10 \end{cases}$

8. $\begin{cases} x + y = 5 \\ 4x + 4y = 20 \end{cases}$

9. $\begin{cases} 3x - 2y = 4 \\ 4x - 5y = 3 \end{cases}$

 **INSTRUCTION**

Matrices

A **matrix** is an array of numbers organized into rows and columns and held by a bracket. Matrices allow you to organize and work with large amounts of information. You can add, subtract, and multiply matrices. You can also use matrices to solve a system of equations. You use capital letters to represent matrices.

A matrix can hold any type of number or variable. Each value in a matrix is called an element or entry. Matrices are identified by their **dimension**, or size. The dimension of a matrix is always given as (number of rows) × (number of columns). For example:

> **Matrices allow us to organize and work with large amounts of information.**

$$A = \begin{bmatrix} -2 & 0 & 3 \\ 6 & 1 & -2 \end{bmatrix}$$

This matrix contains six different elements or entries. It has two rows (across) and three columns (up and down). The dimension of this matrix is 2×3.

A matrix that has the same number of rows as columns is called a **square matrix.** For example, $B = \begin{bmatrix} 2 & -1 & 3 \\ 4 & 0 & -8 \\ 1 & 7 & 3 \end{bmatrix}$ is a square matrix.

Matrices are **equivalent** if they are the same dimension and all corresponding entries are equivalent. The following matrices are equivalent: $C = \begin{bmatrix} 1 & 1.5 \\ 5 & -4 \\ 4.5 & .2 \end{bmatrix}$ and $D = \begin{bmatrix} 1 & \frac{3}{2} \\ 5 & -4 \\ 4\frac{1}{2} & \frac{1}{5} \end{bmatrix}$.

The addition and subtraction of matrices is done much like the addition and subtraction of numbers. To add and subtract matrices, you must first make sure they are the same dimension. If they are not, the matrices cannot be added or subtracted. Next, you add (or subtract) the corresponding entries. This means that you add the entry in the first row, first column in one matrix with the entry in the first row, first column in the second matrix and put the result

39

in a new matrix, first row, first column. Order is not important unless you are subtracting matrices. Matrix addition is commutative.

Example 1

Add the following matrices.

$$\begin{bmatrix} 1 & 5 \\ -8 & 7 \\ 6 & 0 \end{bmatrix} + \begin{bmatrix} 10 & 4 \\ 2 & -4 \\ 3 & 0 \end{bmatrix}$$

1. First, determine if the matrices can be combined. Because both of these matrices have the same dimension (3 × 2), they can be added together.

2. Add all corresponding entries, and put the results in the same spot in the resulting matrix:

$$\begin{bmatrix} 1+10 & 5+4 \\ -8+2 & 7+-4 \\ 6+3 & 0+0 \end{bmatrix} = \begin{bmatrix} 11 & 9 \\ -6 & 3 \\ 9 & 0 \end{bmatrix}$$

Subtraction of matrices is done the same way except that the values are subtracted instead of added. One way to make sure no sign errors are made is to change the subtraction to addition and change the sign of every entry in the second matrix. Be careful of your signs!

Multiplication of matrices is a little more complicated. First, two matrices can be multiplied only if the number of columns in the first matrix is equal to the number of rows in the second matrix. Order is extremely important when multiplying matrices. Matrix multiplication is not commutative.

Example 2

Multiply the following matrices.

$$\begin{bmatrix} 2 & -1 \\ 3 & 0 \end{bmatrix} \begin{bmatrix} 1 & 3 & 0 \\ -2 & 4 & 1 \end{bmatrix}$$

1. Determine if matrix multiplication is possible by looking at the dimensions of each matrix:

   2×2 2×3
   first matrix   second matrix

   Because the "inner" two dimensions match, these matrices can be multiplied. Also, by looking at the "outer" dimensions, you can determine that the product matrix will be 2×3.

2. Multiply the first row of the first matrix with every column of the second matrix. Think of flipping the row on its side and multiplying the numbers that are next to each other. Multiplying row one times column one will result in the entry for row one, column one in the product matrix.

$$\begin{bmatrix} 2 & -1 \\ 3 & 0 \end{bmatrix} \begin{bmatrix} (2)1 & (2)3 & (2)0 \\ (-1)-2 & (-1)4 & (-1)1 \end{bmatrix} =$$

$$\begin{bmatrix} (2)(1)+(-1)(-2) & (2)(3)+(-1)(4) & (2)(0)+(-1)(1) \end{bmatrix} = \begin{bmatrix} 2+2 & 6-4 & 0-1 \end{bmatrix}$$

$$\Rightarrow \begin{bmatrix} 4 & 2 & -1 \end{bmatrix}$$

3. Multiply the second row of the first matrix with every column of the second matrix. The results will make up the second row of the product matrix.

$$\begin{bmatrix} 2 & -1 \\ 3 & 0 \end{bmatrix} \begin{bmatrix} (3)1 & (3)3 & (3)0 \\ (0)-2 & (0)4 & (0)1 \end{bmatrix} = \begin{bmatrix} 4 & 2 & -1 \\ (3)(1)+(0)(-2) & (3)(3)+(0)(4) & (3)(0)+(0)(1) \end{bmatrix}$$

$$= \begin{bmatrix} 4 & 2 & -1 \\ 3+0 & 9+0 & 0+0 \end{bmatrix} \Rightarrow \begin{bmatrix} 4 & 2 & -1 \\ 3 & 9 & 0 \end{bmatrix}$$

The matrix above is the final product matrix. Its dimensions are 2×3, as indicated when you first inspected the dimensions.

When multiplying matrices, it is important to remember the following:

1. Always check to see if multiplication is possible and, if it is, determine what size your product matrix will be.

2. Always multiply the first row by every column of the second matrix—first times first, second times second, and so forth. Try to think of tipping the row on its side and multiply the numbers that would end up next to each other.

3. Never move to the second row until you have multiplied every column by the row before.

4. Matrix multiplication is not commutative.

Matrices can also be used to solve systems of equations. We will look at one way matrices are used to solve a system. Before we do, however, we must look at **determinants**. Every square matrix has a whole number associated with it called a determinant. This number will be used to solve a system of equations.

When finding the determinant of a matrix, the brackets around the matrix are replaced by two lines: $\begin{bmatrix} 3 & -7 \\ 2 & 4 \end{bmatrix} \Rightarrow \begin{vmatrix} 3 & -7 \\ 2 & 4 \end{vmatrix}$

Basically, finding the determinant of a matrix consists of multiplying along a diagonal and subtracting a top total from a bottom total.

Example 3

Find the determinant of the following 2×2 matrix: $\begin{bmatrix} 4 & 2 \\ 1 & 3 \end{bmatrix}$

1. Multiply the diagonals: $\begin{vmatrix} 4 & 2 \\ 1 & 3 \end{vmatrix}$ 2

    12

2. Subtract: bottom − top

$$12 - 2 = 10$$

The determinant of this matrix is 10.

Although finding the determinant of a 3×3 matrix is slightly more involved, the basic concept is the same: Multiply diagonals and subtract.

Example 4

Find the determinant of the following 3×3 matrix: $\begin{bmatrix} 1 & 2 & -3 \\ 4 & 0 & 1 \\ 3 & -2 & 1 \end{bmatrix}$

1. Copy over the first two columns exactly as they appear.

$$\begin{vmatrix} 1 & 2 & -3 \\ 4 & 0 & 1 \\ 3 & -2 & 1 \end{vmatrix} \begin{matrix} 1 & 2 \\ 4 & 0 \\ 3 & -2 \end{matrix}$$

2. Draw six diagonals across all five columns of numbers—three going down and three going up. Begin the down diagonals at the upper left. Begin the up diagonals at the bottom left.

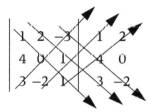

3. Multiply along the diagonals:

   The bottom results are: 0 6 24   The top results are: 0 −2 8

4. Add the bottom numbers, and add the top numbers:

   The bottom: 30   The top: 6

5. Subtract: (Sum of the Bottom) − (Sum of the Top)

   $30 - (-6) = 36$

   The determinant of this matrix is 36.

These values can be used to solve a system of equations. The method known as **Cramer's Rule** uses the determinants of matrices to determine the solution to a system of two or three equations.

43

Example 5

Solve the following system of equations using Cramer's Rule:

$$\begin{cases} -2x + y = -4 \\ 3x + y = 11 \end{cases}$$

1. Set up three determinants: D, D_x, D_y.

   D is the determinant matrix made up of the coefficients of the equations, exactly as they appear: $\begin{vmatrix} -2 & 1 \\ 3 & 1 \end{vmatrix}$.

   D_x is the determinant matrix where the coefficients of the x terms are replaced with the values on the opposite side of the equations: $\begin{vmatrix} -4 & 1 \\ 11 & 1 \end{vmatrix}$.

   D_y is the determinant matrix where the coefficients of the y terms are replaced with the values on the other side of the equations: $\begin{vmatrix} -2 & -4 \\ 3 & 11 \end{vmatrix}$.

   Note: Pay special attention to signs when you set up your determinants.

2. Find the determinant of each matrix, using the steps discussed above:

   $D = -5$ $\qquad\qquad$ $D_x = -15$ $\qquad\qquad$ $D_y = -10$

3. Find the x and y coordinates by dividing:

   $x = \dfrac{D_x}{D}$ and $y = \dfrac{D_y}{D}$:

   $x = \dfrac{-15}{-5} = 3$ $\qquad\qquad$ $y = \dfrac{-10}{-5} = 2$

   The solution to this system is (3, 2).

Practice Activities

Perform the following operations.

1. Add or subtract the following matrices if possible.

    a. $\begin{bmatrix} 2 & 3 & -1 \\ 7 & 9 & 2 \\ 5 & 2 & 4 \end{bmatrix} + \begin{bmatrix} -2 & -1 & -8 \\ 5 & 9 & 0 \\ 5 & 2 & 1 \end{bmatrix}$

    b. $\begin{bmatrix} 2 & 1 \\ 4 & 6 \end{bmatrix} - \begin{bmatrix} 3 & 1 & 3 \\ 0 & 3 & 6 \end{bmatrix}$

2. Multiply if possible. $\begin{bmatrix} -2 & 4 \\ 1 & 8 \\ 6 & 4 \end{bmatrix} \begin{bmatrix} 3 & 1 \\ 5 & 4 \end{bmatrix}$

3. Multiply if possible. $\begin{bmatrix} 3 & 3 & 6 \\ -1 & 2 & 7 \\ 1 & 0 & 3 \end{bmatrix} \begin{bmatrix} 2 & 3 \\ 3 & -2 \\ 0 & 1 \end{bmatrix}$

4. Find the determinant of each of the following matrices.

    a. $\begin{bmatrix} 2 & -3 \\ 1 & 0 \end{bmatrix}$

    b. $\begin{bmatrix} 4 & 3 & 2 \\ -1 & -2 & 0 \\ 2 & 8 & 5 \end{bmatrix}$

    c. $\begin{bmatrix} 5 & 0 & 1 \\ 6 & -3 & 2 \\ 7 & 4 & 2 \end{bmatrix}$

5. Solve using Cramer's Rule. $\begin{cases} y = -3x + 3 \\ -x + 2y = 6 \end{cases}$

 **INSTRUCTION**

Roots and Radicals

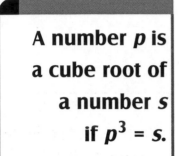

A number *p* is a cube root of a number *s* if *p*³ = *s*.

A number x is a **square root** of a number n if $x^2 = n$. n in this case would be called a perfect square. A number p is a cube root of a number s if $p^3 = s$. In this case, s would be called a perfect cube. The symbol $\sqrt{\ }$ is called the **radical** sign. A square root radical is considered simplified if (a) there are no perfect square factors left inside the radical other than 1 and (b) there are no radicals in the denominator. Occasionally, you will need to rationalize the denominator in order to eliminate any radicals in the denominator. To do this, you should multiply both the top and bottom of a radical by whatever is in the denominator.

Example 1

Simplify the radical $\sqrt{24}$.

Solution:

1. First, find the prime factors of the number 24.

   $24 = 2 \cdot 2 \cdot 2 \cdot 3$

2. List these factors inside the radical.

   $\sqrt{2 \cdot 2 \cdot 2 \cdot 3}$

3. Because you are finding the square root of 24, look for any factors that are the same. For every pair you find, cross out the factors and write that number on the outside once. In this problem, there are two 2s. Cross them both out, and write the number 2 outside the radical, showing that 2 is a perfect square factor of 24. The remaining factors do not have a match (and therefore are not perfect square factors), so they must remain inside the radical.

   $2\sqrt{2 \cdot 3}$

   There are no other perfect squares inside the radical, so $\sqrt{24}$ is simplified to $2\sqrt{6}$.

   Note: To simplify radicals that are being multiplied, such as $\sqrt{50} \cdot \sqrt{32}$, you should first multiply the two radicals, and then follow the steps above to simplify.

Example 2

Simplify the radical $\sqrt[3]{54x^4y^7}$.

Solution:

1. First, find the prime factors of the number $54x^4y^7$.

    $54x^4y^7 = 3 \cdot 3 \cdot 3 \cdot 2 \cdot x \cdot x \cdot x \cdot x \cdot y \cdot y \cdot y \cdot y \cdot y \cdot y \cdot y$

2. List these factors inside the radical.

    $$\sqrt[3]{3 \cdot 3 \cdot 3 \cdot 3 \cdot 2 \cdot x \cdot x \cdot x \cdot x \cdot y \cdot y \cdot y \cdot y \cdot y \cdot y \cdot y}$$

3. $\sqrt[3]{}$ indicates that you are finding the cube root of $54x^4y^7$. The 3 in this case is called the index. In order to find the cube root, look for groups of three factors that are the same. For every three factors you find that are the same, cross them out and write that number on the outside once. From this problem, you will notice there are 3 of 3's, 3 x's, and 2 sets of 3 y's. Cross out all 3 of each, and write the number 3 and the variables x, y, and y outside the radical once. Everything else should be left inside the radical.

    $3 \cdot x \cdot y \cdot y\sqrt[3]{2 \cdot x \cdot y}$

    There are no other perfect cubes inside the radical so

    $\sqrt[3]{54x^4y^7}$ is simplified to $3xy^2\sqrt{2xy}$.

    Note: The **index** of a radical determines how many of one factor you need in order to write it on the outside of the radical. For example, $\sqrt[5]{}$ indicates you are looking for factors inside the radical in groups of 5; for $\sqrt[7]{}$ you would need groups of 7.

Example 3

Simplify the radical $\sqrt{\dfrac{7}{11}}$.

Solution:

1. First, look to see if you can reduce the fraction or if there are any perfect squares you can simplify. In this example, there is nothing you can reduce and there are no perfect squares, so you should separate the radical into two radicals: one in the numerator and one in the denominator.

$$\frac{\sqrt{7}}{\sqrt{11}}$$

2. To eliminate the radical in the denominator, you must rationalize the denominator by multiplying both the numerator and denominator by $\sqrt{11}$.

$$\frac{\sqrt{7}}{\sqrt{11}} \cdot \frac{\sqrt{11}}{\sqrt{11}}$$

This is the equivalent of multiplying by one and will create a perfect square in the denominator, which can be simplified to a whole number.

$$\frac{\sqrt{7}}{\sqrt{11}} \cdot \frac{\sqrt{11}}{\sqrt{11}} = \frac{\sqrt{77}}{\sqrt{121}} \Rightarrow \frac{\sqrt{77}}{11}$$

There are no perfect squares left in the numerator, and there are no radicals in the denominator; therefore, this radical is in simplest form.

Example 4

Simplify the radical $\sqrt[4]{\dfrac{3}{8}}$.

Solution:

1. First, look to see if you can reduce the fraction or if there are any perfect squares you can simplify. In this example, there is nothing you can reduce, and there are no perfect squares, so you should separate the radical into two radicals: one in the numerator and one in the denominator.

$$\frac{\sqrt[4]{3}}{\sqrt[4]{8}}$$

2. To eliminate the radical in the denominator, you must rationalize the denominator by multiplying both the numerator and denominator by $\sqrt[4]{2}$.

$$\frac{\sqrt[4]{3}}{\sqrt[4]{2 \cdot 2 \cdot 2}} \cdot \frac{\sqrt[4]{2}}{\sqrt[4]{2}}$$

This will give the denominator 4 factors of 2, or $\sqrt[4]{16}$. This can be simplified to 2.

$$\frac{\sqrt[4]{3}}{\sqrt[4]{2 \bullet 2 \bullet 2}} \bullet \frac{\sqrt[4]{2}}{\sqrt[4]{2}} = \frac{\sqrt[4]{6}}{\sqrt[4]{16}} \Rightarrow \frac{\sqrt[4]{6}}{2}$$

There are no 4th roots in the numerator, and there are no radicals left in the denominator; therefore, this radical is in simplest form.

Example 5

Simplify the radical $\dfrac{\sqrt{3}}{6 - \sqrt{2}}$.

Solution:

1. To eliminate the radical in the denominator, you must rationalize the denominator by multiplying both the numerator and denominator by $6 + \sqrt{2}$.

$$\frac{\sqrt{3}}{6 - \sqrt{2}} \bullet \frac{6 + \sqrt{2}}{6 + \sqrt{2}}$$

The reason for multiplying by $6 + \sqrt{2}$ is it eliminates the middle terms when you use **foil**. If you multiplied by $6 - \sqrt{2}$, you would still have a radical in the denominator.

$$\frac{\sqrt{3}}{6 - \sqrt{2}} \bullet \frac{6 + \sqrt{2}}{6 + \sqrt{2}} = \frac{6\sqrt{3} + \sqrt{6}}{36 - 2} \Rightarrow \frac{6\sqrt{3} + \sqrt{6}}{34}$$

There are no radicals in the numerator that can be simplified, and there are no radicals left in the denominator; therefore, this radical is in simplest form.

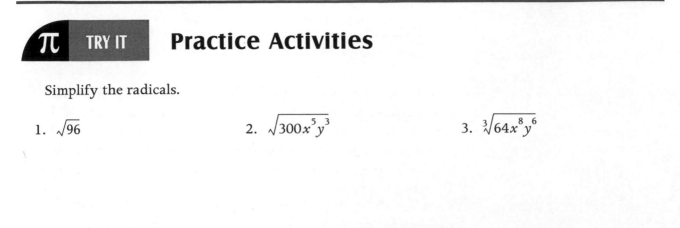

π TRY IT   **Practice Activities**

Simplify the radicals.

1. $\sqrt{96}$

2. $\sqrt{300x^5y^3}$

3. $\sqrt[3]{64x^8y^6}$

4. $\sqrt[5]{64x^{10}y^7}$

5. $\sqrt{\dfrac{25}{4}}$

6. $\sqrt{\dfrac{36}{7}}$

7. $\sqrt{18} \cdot \sqrt{20}$

8. $\dfrac{13}{5 + \sqrt{3}}$

9. $\dfrac{\sqrt{5}}{1 + \sqrt{6}}$

√ **INSTRUCTION**

Polynomials

> A function with many terms is called a polynomial function.

A function with many terms is called a **polynomial** function. In order to be classified a polynomial function, the **exponents** of the function will all be whole numbers and the coefficients will all be real numbers. To write a polynomial function in standard form, you must list the terms by their exponents from greatest to least.

There are two ways to classify polynomials: by the number of terms and the degree. To classify by the number of terms, first combine like terms. If the function has one term, it is called a **monomial,** two terms is a **binomial,** and three terms is a **trinomial.** Everything else falls under the general term polynomial.

To classify a polynomial by its degree, you would identify its highest exponent. A polynomial of which the highest exponent is 4 is called **quartic.** One of which the highest exponent is 3 is called **cubic.** If the highest exponent is 2, then it is a **quadratic function.** If the highest exponent is 1, then it is called linear, and if 0 is the highest exponent, then that function is **constant.**

Function	Degree	Terms	Classification
$y = 3x^3 - 5$	3	2	Cubic binomial
$y = 5x^2 - 6x + 2$	2	3	Quadratic trinomial
$y = 6$	0	1	Constant

To add or subtract polynomials, first line up vertically the like terms of what you are adding or subtracting, then add or subtract the coefficients of those like terms. Like terms are terms that have the same variables raised to the same power.

To multiply polynomials, distribute every term from the first function through every term from the second function, then combine like terms.

51

Example 1

$$(5x^2 - 9x - 12) + (13x + 3x^2 - 2)$$

Solution:

1. Line up the two equations vertically in standard form, placing like terms above one another.

$$\begin{array}{r} 5x^2 - 9x - 12 \\ + 3x^2 + 13x - 2 \\ \hline \end{array}$$

2. Add the coefficients.

$$\begin{array}{r} 5x^2 - 9x - 12 \\ + 3x^2 + 13x - 2 \\ \hline 8x^2 + 4x - 14 \end{array}$$

Example 2

$$(6x^2 - 7x + 2x^3 - 9) - (4x + -8x^3 + 2)$$

Solution:

1. Line up the two equations vertically in standard form, placing like terms above one another. You can place a $0x^2$ in the second equation to hold its place.

$$\begin{array}{r} 2x^3 + 6x^2 - 7x - 9 \\ - (-8x^3) + 0x^2 + 4x + 2 \\ \hline \end{array}$$

2. Subtract the coefficients.

$$\begin{array}{r} 2x^3 + 6x^2 - 7x - 9 \\ - (-8x^3) + 0x^2 + 4x + 2 \\ \hline 10x^3 + 6x^2 - 11x - 11 \end{array}$$

Example 3

$$(3x^2 + 4)(2x^2 + 5x - 3)$$

Solution:

1. Distribute the $3x^2$ and the 4 through every term in the second function.

$$2x^2(3x^2) + 5x(3x^2) - 3(3x^2) + 2x^2(4) + 5x(4) - 3(4)$$

2. Simplify the expression.

$$6x^4 + 15x^3 - 9x^2 + 8x^2 + 20x - 12 \implies$$

$$6x^4 + 15x^3 - 1x^2 + 20x - 12$$

3. Write your simplified expression in standard form.

$$6x^4 + 15x^3 - 1x^2 + 20x - 12$$

Example 4

$$(2x^2 + 7)(x^2 - 3)$$

Solution:

1. Distribute the $2x^2$ and the 7 through every term in the second function.

$$x^2(2x^2) - 3(2x^2) + x^2(7) - 3(7)$$

2. Simplify the expression.

$$2x^4 - 6x^2 + 7x^2 - 21 \implies 2x^4 + x^2 - 21$$

3. Write your simplified expression in standard form.

$$2x^4 + x^2 - 21$$

Example 5

$$(3a^2b + 2a)(ab^2 - 5b + 4a^2b^2)$$

Solution:

1. Distribute the $3a^2b$ and the $2a$ through every term in the second function.

$$(3a^2b)\,ab^2 - (3a^2b)\,5b + (3a^2b)\,4a^2b^2$$

$$(2a)\,ab^2 - (2a)\,5b + (2a)\,4a^2b^2$$

2. Simplify the expression.

$$3a^3b^3 - 15a^2b^2 + 12a^4b^3 + 2a^2b^2 - 10ab + 8a^3b^2$$

3. Combine like terms, and write your simplified expression in standard form.

$$12a^4b^3 + 3a^3b^3 + 8a^3b^2 - 13a^2b^2 - 10ab$$

Practice Activities

Classify.

1. $4x^4 + 3x - 7$

2. $7x^2 + 9$

3. $10x^3$

Perform the indicated operation.

4. $(5x^2 - 7x + 3) + (8x - 4x^2 + 1)$

5. $(12x^3 - 7x + 5) - (6x^3 - 2x^2)$

6. $(3x - 2)(5x^2 - 9x - 10)$

7. $(2x^2)(4x^3 - 2x^2 - 3x + 4)$

8. $(7xy^2 - 1x^4)(4x^3y + 3y^2)$

9. $(5x^2 - 9 + 2x) + (4x - 3x^2 + 1)$

10. $(11x^3 - 7x^2 + 5) - (8x^2 - 10x^3 + 2)$

INSTRUCTION

Factoring Polynomials

When we factor a polynomial, we are finding the pieces that multiply together to make that polynomial.

To factor a polynomial means to separate it into its smallest, most basic, pieces. As you may recall, a factor is a number or term that divides evenly into another number or term. When you factor a polynomial, you are finding the pieces that multiply together to make that polynomial.

There are several different methods of factoring. Often, the number of terms in the polynomial to be factored will determine which method you should try. Remember, not all polynomials can be factored. Polynomials that cannot be broken down at all are called prime.

Factoring out the greatest common factor: The **greatest common factor** (GCF) of a polynomial is the largest number that will divide evenly into every term in the polynomial, along with the variable to the largest degree that will divide evenly into every term. Consider the polynomial $4a^4b^2 + 16a^3b^4 - 8a^2b^3$. First, looking at the coefficients only, you can see that 4 is the largest number that will divide evenly into 4, 16, and 8. Next, notice that each term contains the variable a. In order to determine the highest degree of a that will divide into every term evenly, you must choose the lowest power that you see (you cannot divide 4 a's into 2 a's). Therefore, the highest power of a that divides into each term is a^2. Following the same reasoning, the highest power of b that divides into every term is b^2. The GCF for this polynomial is $4a^2b^2$.

To factor using this GCF, divide every term by it and write the final result as a product of the GCF and the polynomial.

Example 1

Factor the polynomial: $4a^4b^2 + 16a^3b^4 - 8a^2b^3$.

1. Determine the GCF: $4a^2b^2$

2. Divide every term in the polynomial by the GCF:

$$\frac{4a^4b^2}{4a^2b^2} + \frac{16a^3b^4}{4a^2b^2} - \frac{8a^2b^3}{4a^2b^2}.$$

55

3. Write the final result as a product of the GCF and the remaining polynomial: $4a^2b^2(a^2 + 4ab^2 - 2b)$.

You can check to see if you have factored correctly by multiplying your result. You should get back what you started with.

Factoring the difference of two squares: You can apply this method if the polynomial you are factoring fits this description: (1) It is a binomial. (2) Terms are separated by a subtraction sign. (3) Both terms involved are perfect squares. Most of us are familiar with perfect square numbers: 1, 4, 9, 16, 25, ... To determine if a variable is a perfect square, check to see if the exponent is divisible by two. If it is, then the term is a perfect square and the square root is the result when you have divided the exponent by two.

To factor the **difference of two squares**, apply a pattern: $a^2 - b^2 = (a - b)(a + b)$, where a^2 and b^2 are perfect squares and a and b are their square roots.

Example 2

Factor the polynomial $4a^2 - b^6$.

1. Check to be sure that it fits the criteria: (1) It is a binomial. (2) The terms are separated by a subtraction sign. (3) $4a^2$ is a perfect square and the exponent of 6 is divisible by 2, so b^6 must also be a perfect square (with a square root of b^3).

2. Take the square roots of each term, and apply the pattern: The square root of the first term is $2a$, and the square root of the second is b^3. The factored form of the given polynomial is $(2a - b^3)(2a + b^3)$.

3. Again, multiplying your final result should give you what you started with.

Factoring the sum or difference of two cubes: You can apply this method if the polynomial you are factoring fits this description: (1) It is a binomial. (2) Terms are separated by a plus or a minus sign. (3) Both terms involved are perfect cubes. You may have to make a list of perfect cubes to refer to because you may not be as familiar with them. Also, if a variable is a perfect cube, its exponent is divisible by 3.

To factor the **sum or difference of two cubes**, apply this pattern: $a^3 - b^3 = (a - b)(a^2 + ab + b^2)$, where a^3 and b^3 are perfect cubes and a and b are their cube roots. An easier way to think of this is to follow the following steps:

1. The binomial is always formed by the cube roots, using the same sign as in the original problem.

2. The trinomial is built off of this binomial with the following steps:

   a. Square the first term.

   b. Change the sign.

   c. Multiply the two terms.

   d. Square the last term.

Example 3

Factor the following polynomial: $8a^3 + b^6$.

1. Check to see that it fits the criteria: (1) It is a binomial. (2) Terms are separated by a plus sign. (3) $8a^3$ is a perfect cube and, because 6 is divisible by 3, b^6 is also a perfect cube.

2. Take the cube roots and apply the pattern: The cube root of $8a^3$ is $2a$ and the cube root of b^6 is b^2. The roots form the binomial $(2a \quad b^2)$, and building off that, you get $(4a^2 + 2ab^2 + b^4)$. The final result is $(2a - b^2)(4a^2 + 2ab + b^4)$.

3. Multiplying this binomial and trinomial should result in the original polynomial.

   Factoring trinomials: You can apply this method when you are attempting to factor any trinomial. This effort involves a lot of guess and check, but you will find that you become better at "guessing" once you have practiced it. Trinomials will factor into two binomials where the first terms in each will multiply to the first term of the trinomial, the last terms in each will multiply to the last term in the trinomial, and the inside/outside terms (think of foil) will combine to make the middle term of the trinomial.

Example 4

Factor the polynomial: $6x^2 + 11x + 4$.

1. Determine your signs: Because the second sign is positive in this trinomial, both of the signs in the binomials will be the same. Because the middle term is positive, they will both be positive. If the middle term was negative, both signs would have been negative. If the second sign was negative, then each sign in the binomials would be different (one + and one −). So far this is known: (+)(+).

2. Consider options: The front terms must multiply to $6x^2$. Your options are $2x$ and $3x$ or $6x$ and $1x$. The back terms must multiply to the last term in the trinomial, 4. Your options are 2 and 2, or 4 and 1. Here are some of the possibilities:

   $(3x + 4)(2x + 1)$ or $(6x + 1)(x + 4)$ or $(2x + 2)(3x + 2)$ or $(6x + 2)(x + 2)$

3. Multiply the inside outside terms (foil) to see which combination is correct:

   First option: $8x + 3x = 11x$

   Second option: $1x + 24x = 25x$

   Third option: $6x + 4x = 10x$

   Fourth option: $2x + 12x = 14x$

   Because the first combination resulted in $11x$ (our middle term), that is the correct combination. Your final answer is $(3x + 4)(2x + 1)$.

4. Multiplying the final result will give you back the polynomial you started with.

Multiplying using grouping: You can apply **grouping** when you have four terms to factor. This method involves factoring out a GCF from each binomial and then finding a common binomial factor. You may have to rearrange terms to apply this method.

Example 5

Factor the polynomial: $3ab + 12a - 5b - 20$.

1. Separate the polynomial into two binomials: $(3ab + 12a) +$ $(-5b - 20)$. Notice that the subtraction sign was pushed inside the parentheses and a plus was added in between. No other signs need to change.

2. Factor out a GCF from each polynomial: $3a(b + 4) - 5(b + 4)$. A negative 5 was factored out because the signs should match the first binomial.

3. Find a common binomial factor: $(b + 4)$.

4. Write your final result as a product of the common binomial factor and the remaining terms: $(b + 4)(3a - 5)$.

5. Multiplying your final result should result in the original polynomial.

You can use factoring to solve polynomial equations that are factorable. First, factor the polynomial and then set each factor $= 0$ to find the solutions.

Solve: $2x^2 + 12x = 32$

1. Make sure the equation is set equal to zero: $2x^2 + 12x - 32 = 0$.

2. Factor the left side of the equation using one of the methods discussed (or a combination of methods): Here, you must first factor out a GCF and then you can factor the trinomial. $2(x^2 + 6x - 16) \Rightarrow 2(x + 8)(x - 2) = 0$.

3. The **zero product property** states that, if $ab = 0$ then $a = 0$, $b = 0$, or both must equal 0. Therefore, you can set each factor *with a variable* equal to 0: $x + 8 = 0$ and $x - 2 = 0$ to find the solutions.

4. Solving each equation, you find that $x = -8$ or $x = 2$.

5. You can check your results by plugging each into the original equation.

$x = 2$	$x = -8$
$2(2^2) + 12(2) = 32$	$2(-8^2) + 12(-8) = 32$
$2 \cdot 4 + 24 = 32$	$2 \cdot 64 + (-96) = 32$
$8 + 24 = 32$	$128 - 96 = 32$
$32 = 32$	$32 = 32$

 **Practice Activities**

Factor each polynomial.

1. $x^4 - 9y^2$

2. $21x^5y^4 + 18x^4y^2 - 24xy$

3. $27x^3 - y^3$

4. $x^2 - 29x + 100$

5. $c^2 - cx + cd - dx$

6. $3x^4 - 24x$

7. $25 - y^2$

8. $3x^2 - 11x + 6$

Solve the following:

9. $x^2 + 9x = 36$

10. $8x^2 - 18 = 0$

INSTRUCTION

Completing the Square

Completing the square is another method for finding the solutions of a quadratic equation. Completing the square is typically used when you cannot solve a quadratic function by factoring or by taking the square root. Completing the square allows you to use both of these previous methods by allowing you to create your own **perfect square trinomial** that can be factored into a squared binomial and then solved by taking the square root.

> **Completing the square is typically used when you cannot solve a quadratic function by factoring or by taking the square root.**

Example 1

Solve $x^2 + 8x - 4 = 0$ by completing the square.

Solution:

1. Write the equation in standard form with $a = 1$. (Recall that standard form is $ax^2 + bx + c = 0$.)

   $x^2 + 8x - 4 = 0$

2. Add the 4 to the right side so that the left side is in the form of $ax^2 + bx$.

   $x^2 + 8x + \underline{\quad} = 4$

3. To complete the square, take half of b and square it.

   $x^2 + 8x + \underline{(4)^2} = 4$

4. Be sure to add whatever value you found for c to both sides in order to keep the equation balanced.

   $x^2 + 8x + 16 = 4 + 16$

5. Factor the trinomial into a squared binomial.

   $(x + 4)^2 = 20$

6. Take the square root of both sides.

   $x + 4 = \pm 2\sqrt{5}$

7. Solve for x by subtracting the 4 from both sides.

   $x = \pm 2\sqrt{5} - 4$

The solutions to this problem are $x = -2\sqrt{5} - 4$ and $2\sqrt{5} - 4$.

Example 2

Solve $2x^2 - 8x - 14 = 0$ by completing the square.

Solution:

1. Divide all terms by 2 in order to write the equation in standard form with $a = 1$.

   $x^2 - 4x - 7 = 0$

2. Add the 7 to the right side so that the left side is in the form of $ax^2 + bx$.

   $x^2 - 4x + \underline{} = 7$

3. To complete the square, take half of b and square it.

   $x^2 - 4x + \underline{(2)}^2 = 7$

4. Be sure to add whatever value you found for c to both sides in order to keep the equation balanced.

   $x^2 - 4x + 4 = 7 + 4$

5. Factor the trinomial into a squared binomial.

   $(x - 2)^2 = 11$

6. Take the square root of both sides.

   $x - 2 = \pm\sqrt{11}$

7. Solve for x by adding the 2 to both sides.

   $x = \pm\sqrt{11} + 2$

   The solutions to this problem are $x = \sqrt{11} + 2$ and $-\sqrt{11} + 2$.

Example 3

Solve $x^2 + 12x + 27 = 0$ by completing the square.

Solution:

1. Write the equation in standard form with $a = 1$.

   $x^2 + 12x + 27 = 0$

2. Subtract 27 from each side so that the left side is in the form of $ax^2 + bx$.

$$x^2 + 12x + \underline{} = -27$$

3. To complete the square, take half of b and square it.

$$x^2 + 12x + \underline{(6)}^2 = -27$$

Be sure to add whatever value you found for c to both sides in order to keep the equation balanced.

$$x^2 + 12x + 36 = -27 + 36$$

4. Factor the trinomial into a squared binomial.

$$(x + 6)^2 = 9$$

5. Take the square root of both sides.

$$x + 6 = \pm 3$$

6. Solve for x by subtracting the 6 from both sides.

$$x = \pm 3 - 6$$

The solutions to this problem are $x = -3$ and 9.

Practice Activities

Solve the following quadratic equations by completing the square.

1. $x^2 - 20x + 5 = 0$

2. $2x^2 + 14x - 6 = 0$

3. $x^2 + 9x - 6 = 0$

4. $3x^2 - 24x + 9 = 0$

5. $5x^2 - 3x + 7 = 4x^2 + 8x$

6. $x^2 - 16x + 5 = 0$

INSTRUCTION

The Quadratic Formula

The **quadratic formula** is another method used to solve a quadratic function. You can use the quadratic formula by first writing the function in standard form ($ax^2 + bx + c = 0$) and determining the values for a, b, and c. Then substitute these values into the formula wherever a, b, and c appear. Once the values have been substituted, then simplify the expression to find the 0's of the function. A quadratic function can have one solution, two solutions, or no solution. A way of determining how many solutions a function will have is simplifying inside of the radical. (This portion of the quadratic formula is called the **discriminant**). If the inside of the radical simplifies to a positive number, then the function has 2 solutions. If the inside of the radical simplifies to 0, then the function has 1 solution. If the inside of the radical simplifies to a negative number, then the function has no real solutions.

> **A quadratic function can have one solution, two solutions, or no solution.**

The quadratic formula is $x = \dfrac{-b \pm \sqrt{b^2 - 4ac}}{2a}$.

Example 1

Find the solution(s) for $x^2 - 6x + 3 = 0$ using the quadratic formula.

1. Write the function in standard form if it is not already. In this case, it is already in standard form.

   $x^2 - 6x + 3 = 0$

2. Identify the values of a, b, and c.

   $a = 1$, $b = -6$, and $c = 3$

3. Substitute these values into the quadratic formula wherever they appear.

   $\dfrac{-(-6) \pm \sqrt{(-6)^2 - 4(1)(3)}}{2(1)}$

4. Simplify the expression.

   $\dfrac{-(-6) \pm \sqrt{(-6)^2 - 4(1)(3)}}{2(1)} \Rightarrow \dfrac{-(-6) \pm \sqrt{36 - 12}}{2(1)} \Rightarrow \dfrac{6 \pm \sqrt{24}}{2}$

5. Reduce the radical to its simplest terms by taking out any perfect squares.

$$\frac{6 \pm \sqrt{24}}{2} \quad \Rightarrow \quad \frac{6 \pm 2\sqrt{6}}{2}$$

6. Write the solutions in their simplest form by dividing all three numbers outside of the radical by 2.

$$\frac{6 \pm 2\sqrt{6}}{2} \quad \Rightarrow \quad 3 \pm \sqrt{6}$$

7. The solutions for this function are $3 + \sqrt{6}$ and $3 - \sqrt{6}$.

Example 2

Find the solution(s) for $2x^2 - 3x = 4$ using the quadratic formula.

1. Write the function in standard form by subtracting the 4 from both sides.

$$2x^2 - 3x - 4 = 0$$

2. Identify the values of *a, b,* and *c.*

$a = 2$, $b = -3$, and $c = -4$

3. Substitute these values into the quadratic formula wherever they appear.

$$\frac{-(-3) \pm \sqrt{(-3)^2 - 4(2)(-4)}}{2(2)}$$

4. Simplify the expression.

$$\frac{-(-3) \pm \sqrt{(-3)^2 - 4(2)(-4)}}{2(2)} \quad \Rightarrow \quad \frac{-(-3) \pm \sqrt{9 + 32}}{2(2)} \quad \Rightarrow \quad \frac{3 \pm \sqrt{41}}{4}$$

5. Reduce the radical to its simplest terms by taking out any perfect squares. In this case, there are not any, so the expression will not change.

$$\frac{3 \pm \sqrt{41}}{4}$$

6. There is also no reducing that can be done to any of the numbers outside of the radical. The solutions for this function in simplest form are $\dfrac{3 + \sqrt{41}}{4}$ and $\dfrac{3 - \sqrt{41}}{4}$.

Example 3

Find the solution(s) for $4x^2 + 2x + 3 = 10x$ using the quadratic formula.

1. Write the function in standard form by subtracting $10x$ from both sides.

   $4x^2 - 8x + 3 = 0$

2. Identify the values of a, b, and c.

   $a = 4$, $b = -8$, and $c = 3$

3. Substitute these values into the quadratic formula wherever they appear.

   $$\dfrac{-(-8) \pm \sqrt{(-8)^2 - 4(4)(3)}}{2(4)}$$

4. Simplify the expression by simplifying within the radical.

   $$\dfrac{-(-8) \pm \sqrt{(-8)^2 - 4(4)(3)}}{2(4)} \Rightarrow \dfrac{-(-8) \pm \sqrt{64 - 48}}{2(4)} \Rightarrow \dfrac{8 \pm \sqrt{16}}{8}$$

5. Reduce the radical to its simplest terms by taking out any perfect squares.

   $$\dfrac{8 \pm \sqrt{16}}{8} \Rightarrow \dfrac{8 \pm 4}{8}$$

6. Simplify the expressions individually.

   $$\dfrac{8 + 4}{8} \Rightarrow \dfrac{12}{8} \qquad \dfrac{8 - 4}{8} \Rightarrow \dfrac{4}{8}$$

7. The solutions for this function are $\dfrac{3}{2}$ and $\dfrac{1}{2}$.

Practice Activities

Solve.

1. $3x^2 + 5x - 7 = 0$

2. $6x^2 + 2x - 5 = 0$

3. $7x^2 - 8 = 9x$

4. $2x^2 - 5x + 3 = -4x^2 + 7$

5. $11x^2 - 4x + 1 = 3x^2 + 8$

6. $x^2 - 12x - 4 = 0$